Chicago Cubs Trivia Quiz Book

500 Questions on the North Siders

D1531775

Chris Bradshaw

Front cover image created by headfuzz by grimboid. Check out his great collection of TV, movie and sport-themed posters online at:

https://www.etsy.com/shop/headfuzzbygrimboid

Introduction

Think you know about the Chicago Cubs? Put your knowledge to the test with this collection of quizzes on Wrigley's finest.

The book covers the whole history of the ballclub, from the successful early years and the post war wilderness through to the revival in the 2010s, the glorious 2016 World Series win and beyond.

The biggest names in Cubs history are present and correct so look out for questions on Kris Bryant, Fergie Jenkins, Kyle Schwarber, Ernie Banks, Anthony Rizzo and many, many more.

There are 500 questions in all covering pitchers and pinch hitters, sluggers and stealers, catchers and coaches and much else besides.

Each quiz contains a selection of 20 questions and is either a mixed bag of pot luck testers or is centered on a specific category such as the 1990s or Wrigley Field.

There are easy, medium and hard questions offering something for North Side novices as well as connoisseurs of Cubs history.

You'll find the answers to each quiz below the bottom of the following quiz. For example, the answers to Quiz 1: Pot Luck, are underneath Quiz 2: Pitchers. The only exception is Quiz 25: Pot Luck. The answers to these can be found under the Quiz 1 questions.

All statistics are the for the regular season only unless otherwise stated and are accurate up to the close of the 2019 season.

We hope you enjoy the Chicago Cubs Trivia Quiz Book.

About the Author

Chris Bradshaw has written over 25 quiz books including titles for Britain's biggest selling daily newspaper, The Sun, and The Times (of London). In addition to baseball, he has written extensively on the NFL, soccer, cricket, darts and poker.

He lives in Birmingham, England and has been following Major League Baseball for over 30 years.

Acknowledgements

Many thanks to Ken and Veronica Bradshaw, Heidi Grant, Steph, James, Ben and Will Roe and Graham Nash.

CONTENTS

Quiz 1: Pot Luck

1. Which Cub hit his 200th career home run in a May 6, 2019 game against the Marlins?

2. What color is the letter C on the famous Cubs logo?

3. Which Cub appears on the front cover of the video game MLB The Show 20?

4. Which superstar did the Cubs select with the second overall pick of the 2013 MLB Draft?

5. The Cubs acquired Anthony Rizzo following a trade with which team?

6. Which starting pitcher went in the opposite direction as part of that famous trade?

7. Who holds the franchise record for the most career home runs struck by a Cubs catcher?

8. The Cubs shutout which team by a score of 17-0 on 17 June, 2015?

9. The Cubs' World Series drought that ended in 2016 had lasted how many years?

10. In an August 2014 game against the Cardinals, which reliever became the just the ninth pitcher in team history to record four strikeouts in a single inning?

11. Who was the first Japanese player to play for the Cubs?

12. What was the name of the 1993 film comedy that starred Thomas Ian Nicholas and Gary Busey as Chicago Cubs players?

13. What is the name of the Cubs mascot?

14. Which Cubs pitcher won the NL Cy Young Award in 2015?

15. True or false – Wrigley Field has hosted the National Hockey League's Winter Classic game?

16. In 2010, which pitcher tied a record after starting his career with the Cubs with eight wins and no losses?

17. What color are the numbers on the back of the Cubs' road jersey?

18. What is the name of the ballpark where the Cubs play home Spring Training games?

19. Which Cubs batter's walk-up music is 'Warm It Up' by Kriss Kross? A) Kris Bryant b) Victor Caratini c) Kyle Schwarber

20. Up to and including the 2019 season, the Cubs had won how many National League pennants? a) 13 b) 15 c) 17

Quiz 25: Answers

1. Blue 2. Javier Báez 3. Kerry Wood 4. Tommy La Stella 5. Mark Grace 6. Kevin Tapani 7. Boston Red Sox 8. Kevin Tapani 9. Todd Hollandsworth 10. Sam Jones 11. Chris Denorfia 12. Rich Hill 13. #25 14. True 15. Tyler Colvin 16. #40 17. Yu Darvish 18. Michael Barrett 19. a) 53 games 20. a) Colts

Quiz 2: Pitchers

1. Which pitcher was on the mound to record the final out in Game 7 of the 2016 World Series?

2. Which Cubs closer successfully converted 32 saves in a row during the 2017 season?

3. Whose 180 career saves during an 8-year spell with the Cubs in the 1980s are the most in franchise history?

4. In August 2015, Jake Arrieta threw a no-hitter against which club?

5. In 1971, who became the first Cubs pitcher to win the Cy Young Award?

6. Who was one out away from delivering a perfect game before walking San Diego's Larry Stahl with two down in the bottom of the ninth in a 1972 game against the Padres?

7. Which pitcher won 20 straight games across the 2015 and 2016 seasons?

8. Which right-hander's 270 strikeouts in 1970 are the most in a single season by a Cubs pitcher?

9. Who holds the club record for the most career saves by a left-handed pitcher?

10. On September 14, 2008, which Cubs pitcher threw a no-hitter against the Astros?

11. Which Cubs pitcher won the NL Rookie of the Year Award in 1998?

12. Prior to Jake Arrieta, who was the last Cubs pitcher to record 20 wins in a season?

13. Which reliever went a franchise record 32.2 innings without giving up a run between May and July 1983?

14. Which reliever tied a franchise record in 2006 after pitching in 84 games that season?

15. In 1998, which reliever set a franchise record after recording 51 saves?

16. Who threw a no-hitter in his maiden appearance for the Cubs in a May 1960 game against the Cardinals?

17. Who was the only Cubs pitcher to record a 20-win season during the 1990s?

18. Which pitcher enjoyed a stretch of 364 games without committing an error between 1982 and 1987?

19. In 1969, Fergie Jenkins set a franchise record after starting how many games? a) 40 b) 41 c) 42

20. By what name was the legendary Cubs pitcher James Vaughn better known? a) Giraffe b) Hippo c) Tiger

Quiz 1: Answers

1. Anthony Rizzo 2. Red 3. Javier Báez 4. Kris Bryant 5. San Diego 6. Andrew Cashner 7. Gabby Hartnett 8. Cleveland 9. 108 years 10. Justin Grimm 11. Kosuke Fukudome 12. 'Rookie of the Year' 13. Clark 14. Jake Arrieta 15. True 16. Carlos Silva 17. Red 18. Sloan Park 19. a) Kris Bryant 20. c) 15

Quiz 3: Pot Luck

1. Prior to joining the Cubs, Jon Lester had spells at Boston and what other American League club?

2. Which centerfielder went through the entire 2006 season without committing an error?

3. Cubs manager David Ross won the World Series twice as a player. Once with Chicago and once with which team?

4. Who hit a home run in his first plate appearance at Wrigley Field against the Pirates in September 2019?

5. In the late 2000s, who became the first Cubs manager since the 1930s with a better than .500 record in his first three seasons with the club?

6. The Platinum Gold Glove, which is given to the best defensive player in the league, was won in 2016 by which Cub?

7. In 2006, which Cub became the first player to hit a home run for Team USA in the World Baseball Classic?

8. Which vocalist, best known as the lead singer of Pearl Jam, recorded a 2008 song about the Cubs called 'All The Way'?

9. In April 1978, the Cubs set a National League record after blowing an 11-run lead in an 18-16 loss to which opponent?

10. Who holds the franchise record for the most All-Star appearances with 14?

11. Which Cubs first baseman received All-Star honors in 1993, 1995 and 1997?

12. Which pair of Cubs pitchers both delivered more than 200 strikeouts during the 2002 season?

13. True or false – No Cubs pitcher has ever tossed a perfect game?

14. In July 2015, who became the first pitcher in over 50 years to throw a no-hitter against the Cubs?

15. Which all-time great was the last pitcher to manage that feat against the Cubs, doing so in 1965?

16. In 2013, which Japanese player became just the second Cubs pitcher since 1970 to record a save in his Major League debut?

17. Who successfully stole a base 34 times in a row across the 2000 and 2001 seasons?

18. In August 2011, who became the first Cub to have an inside the park home run at Wrigley Field as his first career homer?

19. Complete the name of the Cubs' High-A, Carolina League farm team. Myrtle Beach...? a) Pelicans b) Penguins c) Piranhas

20. What was the team's original nickname? a) White Caps b) White Knickerbockers c) White Stockings

Quiz 2: Answers

1. Mike Montgomery 2. Wade Davis 3. Lee Smith 4. L.A. Dodgers 5. Fergie Jenkins 6. Milt Pappas 7. Jake Arrieta 8. Fergie Jenkins 9. Randy Myers 10. Carlos Zambrano 11. Kerry Wood 12. Jon Lieber 13. Warren Brusstar 14. Bob Howry 15. Rod Beck 16. Don Cardwell 17. Greg Maddux 18. Lee Smith 19. c) 42 20. a) Hippo

Quiz 4: Batters

1. Who holds the record for hitting the most home runs in team history?

2. How many times did he go yard to set that home run record?

3. Who has the most at-bats in franchise history?

4. Whose 1,316 runs scored are the most in franchise history?

5. Which left-hander's 699 at bats in 2006 are the most by a Cubs hitter in a single season?

6. Whose 30-game hitting streak in 1989 was the longest by a Cubs player since the Second World War?

7. Who set a franchise record in 2015 after striking out 199 times?

8. Whose 27 home runs in 2002 are the most in a single season by a Cubs switch-hitter?

9. Which batter was hit by a pitch a record 30 times during the 2015 season?

10. Which Cubs hitter won seven Silver Slugger Awards between 1984 and 1992?

11. Who holds the franchise record for hitting the most home runs in their rookie season?

12. Which slugger hit two home runs in the 4th inning of a June 2008 game against the White Sox?

13. Who are the two Cubs batters since 1990 to have hit 50 or more doubles in a single season?

14. Who is the only Cubs batter to hit grand slams in back-to-back games?

15. Who set a franchise record during the 2007 season after leading off games with 12 home runs?

16. Which pitcher tied a franchise record in 2006 after slugging six home runs?

17. Which legendary Cub was the first pitcher to hit six home runs in a season?

18. Which Cub holds the Major League record for the most RBIs in a single season?

19. How many RBIs did he register to set that record? a) 189 b) 191 c) 193

20. In an August 1995 game, the Cubs smashed 26 runs against which team? a) Colorado b) New York Mets c) Philadelphia

Quiz 3: Answers

1. Oakland 2. Juan Pierre 3. Boston 4. Nico Hoerner 5. Lou Piniella 6. Anthony Rizzo 7. Derrek Lee 8. Eddie Vedder 9. Philadelphia 10. Ernie Banks 11. Mark Grace 12. Kerry Wood and Matt Clement 13. True 14. Cole Hamels 15. Sandy Koufax 16. Kyuji Fujikawa 17. Eric Young 18. Tony Campana 19. a) Pelicans 20. c) White Stockings

Quiz 5: Pot Luck

1. Who is the only manager to lead the Cubs to the postseason in four successive seasons?

2. Which catcher struck 121 home runs during an eight-season spell with the Cubs between 1981 and 1988?

3. Who was the first Korean to play for the Cubs?

4. The highest scoring game in Major League history was a 26-23 encounter in 1922 between the Cubs and which opponent?

5. Which pitcher made his 400th Major League start in a July 2019 game against the Brewers?

6. In 1979, which Cubs relief pitcher won the NL Cy Young Award?

7. Which celebrated Cub is associated with the phrase, "Let's play two"?

8. Since 1950, who is the only Cubs pitcher to finish an entire season with an ERA of under 2?

9. Who is the youngest Cubs player to receive All-Star recognition?

10. Which Cub was named NL Rookie of the Year for 2015?

11. What is the most common surname of players to have appeared for the Cubs?

12. Who delivered no-hitters in 1969 and 1971, becoming the first Cub in over 80 years to do so?

13. Which right-hander, who spent three seasons in Chicago in the early 2000s, was the first Cubs pitcher to register a save in his Major League debut in the Divisional playoff era?

14. Who threw a no-hitter in just his fourth career start in an April 1972 game against the Phillies?

15. Which 47-year-old reliever, who appeared in three games in 1970, is the oldest person to ever to play for the Cubs?

16. Which Cubs batter made a cameo appearance alongside John Belushi in the 1990 movie comedy 'Taking Care of Business'?

17. The longest game in franchise history lasted how many innings?

18. Who is the play-by-play announcer on Cubs radio broadcasts?

19. What is the highest number of games the Cubs have won in a single season? a) 114 b) 115 c) 116

20. In what year did numbers first appear on Cubs jerseys? a) 1923 b) 1933 c) 1943

Quiz 4: Answers

1. Sammy Sosa 2. 545 times 3. Ernie Banks 4. Ryne Sandberg 5. Juan Pierre 6. Jerome Walton 7. Kris Bryant 8. Mark Bellhorn 9. Anthony Rizzo 10. Ryne Sandberg 11. Kris Bryant 12. Jim Edmonds 13. Mark Grace and Derek Lee 14. Sammy Sosa 15. Alfonso Soriano 16. Carlos Zambrano 17. Fergie Jenkins 18. Hack Wilson 19. b) 191 20. a) Colorado

Quiz 6: Wrigley Field

1. In what year did Wrigley Field host its first Major League game?

2. The outfield walls at Wrigley Field are famously covered in what plant?

3. What was the original name of Wrigley Field?

4. Which opposition batter tied Ty Cobb's record for the most career hits in a 1985 game at Wrigley Field?

5. What color flag with what color letter W is flown above the scoreboard following a Cubs victory?

6. Wrigley Field is the second oldest Major League ballpark. What is the oldest?

7. True or false – No batter has ever hit the famous Wrigley Field scoreboard?

8. What number appears on the flag which flies at the top of the left-field foul pole?

9. By what name is Wrigley Field sometimes known – 'The Friendly...'?

10. In what year was the first night game played at Wrigley Field?

11. Who famously smashed an enormous home run over Waveland Avenue in an epic 1979 game against the Phillies?

12. Gary Pressy played what important role at Wrigley Field between 1987 and 2019?

13. Which Hall of Famer holds the record for the most home runs at Wrigley Field by a visiting player?

14. True or false – Wrigley Field has never hosted the All-Star Game?

15. Who are the two Cubs batters to have hit 290 or more home runs at Wrigley Field?

16. Do the Cubs have a winning or losing record in games played at Wrigley Field?

17. Do the Cubs have a winning or losing record in night games played at Wrigley Field?

18. In 2005, which singer, backed by the Coral Reefer Band, played the first ever rock concert held at Wrigley Field?

19. The deepest point of Wrigley Field is the centerfield wall which is how many feet from home plate? a) 396 b) 398 c) 400

20. Wrigley Field is located on which street? a) East Addison Street b) North Addison Street c) West Addison Street

Quiz 5: Answers

1. Joe Maddon 2. Jody Davis 3. Hee-Seop Choi 4. Philadelphia 5. Jon Lester 6. Bruce Sutter 7. Ernie Banks 8. Jake Arrieta 9. Starlin Castro 10. Kris Bryant 11. Smith (there have been 16 Smiths) 12. Ken Holtzman 13. Todd Wellemeyer 14. Burt Hooton 15. Hoyt Wilhelm 16. Mark Grace 17. 22 innings 18. Pat Hughes 19. c) 116 games 20. b) 1933

Quiz 7: Pot Luck

1. The so-called 'I-55 Rivalry' is between the Cubs and which team?

2. Which Cubs pitching great was on the coaching staff for team South Africa at the World Baseball Classic in 2006?

3. Who are the three Cubs shortstops to have hit 100 home runs?

4. Do the Cubs have a winning or losing record in games played against the Chicago White Sox?

5. The Cubs suffered the worst loss in franchise history in September 1975. Which opponent routed them by a score of 22-0?

6. Hall of Famer Andre Dawson wore what number jersey while with the Cubs?

7. Which pitcher started his career with the Cubs in 2012 with an 0-9 record?

8. In 1970, which pair of pitchers were the first in franchise history to record over 200 strikeouts in a single season?

9. In an August 1995 game against the Dodgers, who hit the 10,000th home run in team history?

10. True or false – The NFL's Chicago Bears played their home games at Wrigley Field between 1921 and 1970?

11. In 1989, who became the first Cub in 27 years to win the NL Rookie of the Year Award?

12. Which Cub, who was tragically killed in a plane crash, was the previous winner of that award in 1962?

13. The Cubs played a game against which team on August 18, 2019 at the Little League World Series?

14. Which pitcher's 197 strikeouts in 2016 were the third most by a Cubs lefty in a single season in club history?

15. Pitcher Kyle Hendricks started his Major League career with which American League organization?

16. Which pitcher's seven starts on Opening Day are a franchise record?

17. After 13 seasons with the Cubs, Mark Grace ended his career with which ballclub?

18. In December 2015, Starlin Castro was traded to which team?

19. What is the most games the Cubs have won in a single month? a) 25 b) 26 c) 27

20. Complete the name of the Cubs' short-season single A farm team. Eugene...? a) Elephants b) Emeralds c) Eskimos

Quiz 6: Answers

1. 1904 2. Ivy 3. Weeghman Park 4. Pete Rose 5. White flag with a blue W 6. Fenway Park 7. True 8. #14 9. Confines 10. 1988 11. Dave Kingman 12. He played the organ 13. Willie Mays 14. False 15. Sammy Sosa and Ernie Banks 16. Winning 17. Winning 18. Jimmy Buffett 19. c) 400ft 20. c) West Addison Street

Quiz 8: 2016 World Champions

1. Which team did the Cubs face in the 2016 World Series?

2. The Cubs won the World Series in how many games?

3. Who was named the 2016 World Series MVP?

4. The Cubs started their 2016 World Championship run by beating which team in the NLDS?

5. The Cubs then claimed the National League pennant by defeating which opponent?

6. Which pitcher was credited with the save in the deciding game of the World Series?

7. Which Cub stole home in Game 1 of the 2016 NLCS?

8. Who hit a leadoff home run in Game 7 of the 2016 World Series?

9. Anthony Rizzo hit a home run in Game 4 of the NLDS after borrowing which teammate's bat?

10. Whose solo home run gave the Cubs a 1-0 win Game 1 of the NLDS?

11. Which country music star led a rendition of 'Go, Cubs, Go' during the 2016 World Series celebration rally?

12. Which Cubs relief pitcher struck a 393-feet home run in Game 2 of the NLDS?

13. Which Cubs pitcher hit a three-run homer in Game 3 of the 2016 NLDS?

14. Which ace was on the receiving end of that home run strike?

15. Who was the Cubs' Designated Hitter during the 2016 World Series?

16. Who tossed a no-hitter against the Reds on April 21, 2016?

17. Given to the NL's best hitter, which Cub won the Hank Aaron Award in 2016?

18. Which pair of Cubs were named co-winners of the NLCS MVP Award?

19. How many games did the Cubs win during the 2016 regular season? a) 101 b) 102 c) 103

20. The most famous rain delay in history occurred in the deciding game of the 2016 World Series. How long did it last? a) 17 minutes b) 27 minutes c) 37 minutes

Quiz 7: Answers

1. St Louis Cardinals 2. Lee Smith 3. Ernie Banks, Shawon Dunston and Javier Báez 4. Losing 5. Pittsburgh 6. #8 7. Chris Volstad 8. Fergie Jenkins and Ken Holtzman 9. Sammy Sosa 10. True 11. Jerome Walton 12. Ken Hubbs 13. Pittsburgh 14. Jon Lester 15. Texas Rangers 16. Fergie Jenkins 17. Arizona 18. New York Yankees 19. b) 26 games 20. b) Emeralds

Quiz 9: Pot Luck

1. Which Cub had the best-selling jersey in baseball during the 2015 season?

2. Who hit a 12th-inning, game-winning home run in his MLB debut against the Rockies in August 2014?

3. In 2017, which Cub received the Roberto Clemente Man of the Year Award?

4. Which Cub hit a famous 1938 home run known as the 'Homer in the Gloamin'?

5. Which former Cub stood in the 1985 Ontario General Election but failed to get elected?

6. Which catcher retired three batters in a row in a brief spell of relief pitching against the Brewers in May 2015?

7. In what country was catcher Willson Contreras born?

8. True or false – Fergie Jenkins played basketball for the Harlem Globetrotters?

9. Which catcher hit a game-tying grand slam in a 6-5 victory over the Cardinals on May 4, 2019?

10. Which Cubs legend had his #10 jersey retired in 2003?

11. True or false – Up to the start of the 2020 season the Cubs hadn't won a single game against the Yankees at Yankee Stadium?

12. Which Cubs catcher pitched a scoreless inning in a July 23, 2018 loss to the Diamondbacks?

13. Whose 2,102 appearances for the Cubs are the most in team history?

14. Do the Cubs have a winning or losing all-time record in road games?

15. What number uniform does Kris Bryant wear?

16. Who is the oldest Cubs player to receive All-Star honors?

17. In a 1991 game against San Francisco, Chico Walker was the last player to achieve what unusual feat?

18. Joe Maddon is one of only three managers to have steered teams to the playoffs at least eight times to have never played in the Majors. Who are the other two?

19. The Cubs endured a woeful start to the 1994 season, beginning the year with how many home losses in a row? a) 10 b) 11 c) 12

20. Complete the name of the Cubs' double AA team. Tennessee...? a) Searchers b) Spiders c) Smokies

Quiz 8: Answers

1. Cleveland 2. Seven 3. Ben Zobrist 4. San Francisco 5. L.A. Dodgers 6. Mike Montgomery 7. Javier Báez 8. Dexter Fowler 9. Matt Szczur's 10. Javier Báez 11. Brett Eldredge 12. Travis Wood 13. Jake Arrieta 14. Madison Bumgarner 15. Kyle Schwarber 16. Jake Arrieta 17. Kris Bryant 18. Javier Báez and Jon Lester 19. c) 103 games 20. a) 17 minutes

Quiz 10: 1980s

1. Which team eliminated the Cubs in the 1984 NLCS?

2. Whose 1,394 hits were the most by a Cubs player during the 1980s?

3. Which Cub won the 1980 NL Batting Title with an average of .324?

4. Who was the manager that guided the Cubs to the 1984 postseason?

5. In August 1982, the Cubs suffered a 2-1 defeat in a 21-inning game against which opponent?

6. Who was the only Cubs batter to hit three home runs in the same game during the 1980s?

7. Which Cubs pitcher was the unanimous choice for the 1984 NL Cy Young Award?

8. Who appeared in 458 games during the 1980s, the most by a Cubs pitcher during the decade?

9. Which fiery relief pitcher received All-Star honors for the only time in his career during a spectacular 1989 season?

10. In a June 1987 game against Houston, who became just the second pair of Cubs in franchise history to hit grand slams in the same game?

11. In 1984, the Cubs acquired pitcher Rick Sutcliffe following a trade with which AL club?

12. Lee Smith was one of two Cubs pitchers to lead the National League in saves during the 1980s. Who was the other?

13. Which team did the Cubs meet in the 1989 NLCS?

14. Who was the manager of that 1989 team?

15. Which Cubs catcher won his only Gold Glove award after an impressive 1986 season?

16. In 1981, owner William Wrigley sold the team to which company for $20.5m?

17. Whose 76 wins were the most by a Cubs pitcher during the 1980s?

18. On August 29, 1989, the Cubs overturned a 9-run deficit to beat which team 10-9 in the 10th inning?

19. What was the highest number of games won by the Cubs during a single regular season during the 1980s? a) 94 b) 95 c) 96

20. How many NL East titles did the Cubs win during the 1980s? a) One b) Two c) Three

Quiz 9: Answers

1. Kris Bryant 2. Javier Báez 3. Anthony Rizzo 4. Gabby Hartnett 5. Fergie Jenkins 6. David Ross 7. Venezuela 8. True 9. Taylor Davis 10. Ron Santo 11. True 12. Victor Caratini 13. Ron Santo 14. Losing 15. #17 16. Ernie Banks 17. He hit an inside-the-park grand slam 18. Joe McCarthy and Jim Leyland 19. a) 10 losses 20. c) Smokies

Quiz 11: Pot Luck

1. Which team defeated the Cubs by a score of 23-22 in a crazy encounter on May 17, 1979?

2. Whose 139 games without an error between 2000 and 2002 is the longest errorless streak by a Cubs catcher?

3. The #31 jersey was retired to honor which pair of Cubs pitchers?

4. True or false – In 1961, the Cubs tried to sign the future New York Jets quarterback Joe Namath?

5. Which Cub delivered a fresh portion of nachos to a St Louis fan after spilling the original order while chasing a foul ball in a game against the Cards in September 2017?

6. In a 1994 game against the Mets, who became the first player in the history of the National League to hit three home runs on opening day?

7. Who was the Mets pitcher on the receiving end of that hat-trick?

8. Who was the first Cub to have his uniform number retired?

9. True or false – Between 1898 and 1902 the team was known as the Chicago Orphans?

10. Who was the first Cub to hit 60 or more home runs in a season more than once?

11. Who are the two Cubs managers to have taken charge of the National League team in the All-Star game this century?

12. Do the Cubs have a winning or losing record in games against American League opponents at Wrigley Field?

13. The Cubs set an unwanted franchise record after losing how many games in August 1999?

14. Who had more wins as manager of the Cubs – Dusty Baker or Joe Maddon?

15. Who holds the club record for the most strikeouts in a season by a left-handed pitcher?

16. In what year did the Cubs play their first regular season game against cross-city rivals the White Sox?

17. The Cubs have won more games against which franchise than any other?

18. Which Cubs pitcher recorded a save in a 1989 game against the Padres without throwing a pitch?

19. What is the highest number of left-handed pitchers to appear for the Cubs in a single season? a) 10 b) 11 c) 12

20. The Cubs were said to be cursed after what animal was denied entrance to a 1945 World Series game at Wrigley Field a) dog b) goat c) sheep

Quiz 10: Answers

1. San Diego 2. Ryne Sandberg 3. Bill Buckner 4. Jim Frey 5. Los Angeles 6. Andre Dawson 7. Rick Sutcliffe 8. Lee Smith 9. Mitch Williams 10. Brian Dayett and Keith Moreland 11. Cleveland 12. Bruce Sutter 13. San Francisco 14. Don Zimmer 15. Jody Davis 16. Tribune Company 17. Rick Sutcliffe 18. Houston 19. c) 96 games 20. b) Two

Quiz 12: Firsts and Lasts

1. The first game in franchise history took place in what year?

2. In what year did the Cubs win their first World Series?

3. Which AL opponent did the Cubs defeat to claim that maiden World Series?

4. Which Cub hit his first Major League pitch for a home run against the Pirates on June 19, 2016?

5. In May 1993, who became the last Cubs batter to hit for the cycle?

6. In 1962, which Cubs second baseman became the first rookie to win a Gold Glove Award?

7. Who was the last Cubs pitcher to hit two home runs in the same game?

8. In what year were the Cubs the National League Wild Card for the first time?

9. In 1970, which Cub became the first National League player to appear in 1,000 straight games?

10. Who was the first Cub to hit 30 home runs and steal 30 bases in the same season?

11. In what decade were Cubs games broadcast on the radio for the first time?

12. In 1987, who became the first Cub to win the Home Run Derby?

13. Who was the first Cubs catcher since Gabby Hartnett in the 1930s to start for the NL in the All-Star game in back-to-back years?

14. In what decade was the first Cubs game shown on television?

15. In 2016, which Cub became the first player in Major League history to win three gold gloves in successive seasons with three different teams?

16. In what year did the Cubs win the NL Central for the first time?

17. In 1958, which Cub became the first player from a team with a losing record to win the NL MVP Award?

18. In 2010, which Cub became the first player born in the 1990s to appear in the Major Leagues?

19. In a 1988 game at Philly, Rick Sutcliffe became the last Cubs pitcher to do what? a) Hit an inside the park homer b) Toss a no-hitter c) Steal home

20. In 2020, the Cubs were scheduled to play their first regular season game in which city a) Dublin b) London c) Rome

Quiz 11: Answers

1. Philadelphia 2. Joe Girardi 3. Greg Maddux and Fergie Jenkins 4. True 5. Addison Russell 6. Tuffy Rhodes 7. Dwight Gooden 8. Ernie Banks 9. True 10. Sammy Sosa 11. Joe Maddon and Dusty Baker 12. Winning 13. 24 games 14. Joe Maddon 15. Jon Lester 16. 1997 17. Braves 18. Mitch Williams 19. b) 11 left-handers 20. b) Goat

Quiz 13: Pot Luck

1. Which Cub won the league MVP award in 1987 despite the team finishing in bottom place in their division?

2. Which Cub hit a three-run homer off Cincinnati's Homer Bailey in his first Major League at bat in May 2010?

3. Who was the only Cubs pitcher to record a 20-win season during the 2000s?

4. Which pitcher hit a grand slam in a September 2008 game against the Mets?

5. Which former Chicago Bears defender was ejected by the home plate umpire while about to sing 'Take Me Out to the Ballgame' during a 2001 game at Wrigley Field?

6. Which Cub was named as one of three shortstops on Major League Baseball's All-Century Team in 1999?

7. Which former Cub was tragically killed in a car crash in Venezuela in 2018?

8. In October 2011, who was appointed the Cubs' Director of Baseball Operations?

9. Which opponent did the Cubs defeat to claim the 1908 World Series?

10. Between May 2002 and May 2003, which Cubs batter smashed five walk-off home runs?

11. Which pitcher had a 16-1 win / loss record during the 1984 season?

12. Greg Maddux joined the 3,000-strikeout club in July 2005 after striking out which San Francisco batter?

13. On April 26, 1941, the Cubs became the first team to do what at their home ballpark?

14. In 1992, the Cubs traded with the White Sox for Sammy Sosa. Which slugger went in the opposite direction?

15. Which Cubs slugger won the Home Run Derby in 1990?

16. Which star infielder made his pitching debut in a July 23, 2018 game against Arizona?

17. Who was appointed as General Manager of the Cubs in October 2011?

18. Which team has beaten the Cubs the most times in franchise history?

19. Which Cubs batter's walk-up music is 'Crank That' by Soulja Bo? a) Yu Darvish b) Willson Contreras c) Addison Russell

20. What is the Cubs' longest home winning streak to start a season? a) 8 wins b) 9 wins c) 10 wins

Quiz 12: Answers

1. 1876 2. 1907 3. Detroit 4. Willson Contreras 5. Mark Grace 6. Ken Hubbs 7. Fergie Jenkins 8. 1998 9. Billy Williams 10. Sammy Sosa 11. 1920s 12. Andre Dawson 13. Willson Contreras 14. 1940s 15. Jason Heyward 16. 2003 17. Ernie Banks 18. Starlin Castro 19. b) Steal home 20. b) London

Quiz 14: 1990s

1. Who was the Cubs' manager at the start of the 1990s?

2. Which first baseman's 1,754 hits were the most by a Cubs player throughout the 1990s?

3. Which Chicago pitcher won the 1992 NL Cy Young Award?

4. Which Cubs catcher enjoyed a career year in 1993 with 73 RBIs, 30 home runs and a batting average of .303?

5. The Cubs had a 162 win, 162 loss record during the 1992 and 1993 seasons under the stewardship of which manager?

6. 'The Dandy Little Glove Man' was the nickname of which second baseman who spent two seasons in Chicago in the late 1990s?

7. Which pitcher set a club record in September 1993 after recording 14 saves, the most in a single month in franchise history?

8. Which Cub won the NL MVP Award in 1998?

9. Which pitcher made his only All-Star appearance in 1996 after enjoying a 13-win season with a 3.03 ERA?

10. True or false – No Cubs batter managed a 200-hit season throughout the whole of the 1990s?

11. Who had a win loss record of 374 to 419 in a five-season spell as team manager between 1995 and 1999?

12. The Cubs were swept 3-0 in the 1998 NLDS by which team?

13. Which versatile Cub played every position apart from pitcher and catcher during the 1998 season?

14. How many division titles did the Cubs win during the 1990s?

15. Whose 50 wins in just three seasons were the second most by a Cubs pitcher during the whole of the 1990s?

16. In Game 3 of the 1998 NLDS, which 21-year-old became the youngest Cubs pitcher to appear in the postseason?

17. How many home runs did Sammy Sosa hit during the 1998 regular season?

18. Which team did the Cubs defeat in a one-game playoff to secure their place in the 1998 Wild Card round?

19. How many winning seasons did the Cubs enjoy during the 1990s? a) Two b) Three c) Four

20. The Cubs started the 1997 season by losing how many consecutive games? a) 12 b) 13 c) 14

Quiz 13: Answers

1. Andre Dawson 2. Starlin Castro 3. Jon Lieber 4. Jason Marquis 5. Steve McMichael 6. Ernie Banks 7. Luis Valbuena 8. Theo Epstein 9. Detroit 10. Alex Gonzalez 11. Rick Sutcliffe 12. Omar Vizquel 13. Play organ music 14. George Bell 15. Ryne Sandberg 16. Anthony Rizzo 17. Jed Hoyer 18. Pittsburgh 19. a) Yu Darvish 20. c) 10 wins (in 1970)

Quiz 15: Pot Luck

1. In a 2002 game against Milwaukee, which Cub became the first player in National League history to hit home runs from both sides of the plate in the same inning?

2. Which pitcher hit a grand slam in a May 2013 game against the White Sox?

3. In 2016, Anthony Rizzo became the second Cubs first baseman to win a Silver Slugger Award. Who was the first?

4. Which leftfielder went 182 consecutive games without committing an error between 2014 and 2016?

5. Which Cubs pitcher tossed a no-hitter against the Braves in August 1969 despite not striking out a single Atlanta batter?

6. Who smashed an enormous home run that landed on a rooftop on Waveland Ave in a game against the Brewers in May 2000?

7. Which Cubs outfielder went 4 for 6 with two home runs and a record 7 RBIs on opening day 2003?

8. Which Washington batter tied a Major League record on May 8, 2016, after walking six times in a game against the Cubs?

9. Joe Maddon set a franchise record in his first season as manager after the Cubs recorded 97 wins. Which manager was the previous holder of that first season wins record which was set in 1984?

10. Which pitcher hit two home runs, seven RBIs and had a batting average of .262 during the 2016 World Championship season?

11. Who was the last Cub with the title of team captain?

12. Which pitcher was one out away from delivering a no-hitter against the Cardinals on September 25, 1995?

13. What number uniform does Anthony Rizzo wear?

14. Who were the two Cubs to hit for the cycle during the 1980s?

15. Who was the oldest player on the Cubs' 2016 World Series team?

16. Who holds the record for the most RBIs in a single season by a Cubs pitcher?

17. Which mid-90s pitcher, who started his pro career as a shortstop, also had 31 hits in 161 at bats while a Cub?

18. True or false – In the 1979 MLB Draft, the Cubs picked future NFL star John Elway?

19. What is the highest number of players the Cubs have used in a single game? a) 26 b) 27 c) 28

20. In their first season, the team played their home games at which ballpark? a) 21st Street Grounds b) 22nd Street Grounds c) 23rd Street Grounds

Quiz 14: Answers

1. Don Zimmer 2. Mark Grace 3. Greg Maddux 4. Rick Wilkins 5. Jim Lefebvre 6. Mickey Morandini 7. Randy Myers 8. Sammy Sosa 9. Steve Trachsel 10. True 11. Jim Riggelman 12. Atlanta 13. Jose Hernandez 14. None 15. Greg Maddux 16. Kerry Wood 17. 66 HRs 18. San Francisco Giants 19. b) Three 20. c) 14

Quiz 16: 2000s

1. Whose 105 wins were the most by a Cubs pitcher during the 2000s?

2. Which batter's 961 hits were the most by a Cubs player during the 2000s?

3. The 2003 Cubs started their playoff run by defeating which team 3 games to 2 in the NLDS?

4. The Cubs fell just short in the 2003 NLCS, losing in seven games to which opponent?

5. How many NL Central titles did the Cubs win during the 2000s?

6. Which Cub won the NL Batting title in 2005 with an average of .335?

7. In 2004, which 24-year-old became the youngest Cubs pitcher selected for the All-Star Game?

8. The Cubs were swept 3-0 in the 2007 NLDS by which team?

9. The Cubs suffered a similar 3-0 NLDS sweep a year later in 2008 at the hands of which team?

10. Which Cub was named the NL Rookie of the Year for 2008?

11. Who was the manager of the Cubs team that reached the 2003 NLCS?

12. In 2006, which centerfielder went through the whole 162-game regular season without committing an error?

13. Of Cubs batters with at least 1,450 at-bats during the decade, who had the best batting average of .304?

14. Which Cub led the NL in 2006 with 204 hits?

15. In 2008, which Cubs batter won the Hank Aaron Award given to the NL's top hitter?

16. Which pitcher made a record 316 appearances during the 2000s?

17. Who were the two Cubs to steal 50 or more bases in a season during the 2000s?

18. Whose 561 runs scored were the most by a Cubs batter during the 2000s?

19. On May 11, 2000, the Cubs were involved in the longest 9-inning game in team history. How long did it last? a) 4hr 12m b) 4hr 22m c) 4hr 32m

20. Which team did the Cubs face in that epic encounter? b) Los Angeles b) Milwaukee c) St Louis

Quiz 15: Answers

1. Mark Bellhorn 2. Travis Wood 3. Derrek Lee 4. Chris Coghlan 5. Ken Holtzman 6. Glenallen Hill 7. Corey Patterson 8. Bryce Harper 9. Jim Frey 10. Jake Arrieta 11. Sammy Sosa 12. Frank Castillo 13. #44 14. Ivan DeJesus and Andre Dawson 15. David Ross 16. Fergie Jenkins 17. Kevin Foster 18. False19. b) 27 players 20. c) 23rd Street Grounds

Quiz 17: Pot Luck

1. Prior to becoming manager of the Cubs, Joe Maddon had been in charge at which club?

2. Who hit a hat-trick of home runs in the 7th, 8th and 9th inning of a 2019 game against the Nationals?

3. Which Cubs batter hit a home run off the opening pitch of the 2018 MLB season?

4. Who tied a Major League record after recording 20 strikeouts in a 1998 game against Houston?

5. Who hit a walk-off grand slam to give the Cubs a 4-3 win over the Nationals on August 12, 2018?

6. Which former Cubs and Indians star threw the ceremonial first pitch at Game 1 of the 2016 World Series?

7. Which pair of pitching brothers combined to give the Cubs a 7-0 shutout win over the Dodgers in an August 1975 matchup?

8. The Cubs play their home Spring Training games in a ballpark in which state?

9. Who was the President of the United States of America when the Cubs played their first game at Wrigley Field?

10. True or false – Manager David Ross finished as the runner up on the 2017 edition of the TV series 'Dancing with the Stars'?

11. Legendary Cub Billy Williams spent the final two years of his Major League career with which American League club?

12. In what year did the Cubs make their last World Series appearance in the 20th century?

13. Which team defeated the Cubs 4-3 in that World Series?

14. Who was the regular closer on the Cubs team that made the playoffs in 1998?

15. Who were the two Cubs to win Silver Slugger Awards during the 1990s?

16. Who holds the team record for the most at-bats for the Cubs in postseason games?

17. What number uniform does Javier Báez wear?

18. Who is the only Cubs pitcher to start for the National League in the All-Star Game? (clue: it was in 1946)

19. The 2012 Cubs endured one of the worst seasons in club history. How many games did they lose? a) 101 b) 102 c) 103

20. In what year was the first Cub game broadcast on WGN-TV? a) 1947 b) 1948 c) 1949

Quiz 16: Answers

1. Carlos Zambrano 2. Aramis Ramirez 3. Atlanta 4. Florida 5. Three 6. Derrek Lee 7. Carlos Zambrano 8. Arizona 9. L.A. Dodgers 10. Geovany Soto 11. Dusty Baker 12. Juan Pierre 13. Derrek Lee 14. Juan Pierre 15. Aramis Ramirez 16. Kyle Farnsworth 17. Juan Pierre and Eric Young 18. Sammy Sosa 19. b) 4hr 22m 20. b) Milwaukee

Quiz 18: 2010s

1. How many NL Central titles did the Cubs win during the 2010s?

2. In 2011, who became the first Cubs third baseman to win a Silver Slugger Award?

3. Who made the most appearances at shortstop for the Cubs during the 2010s?

4. Who hit the most home runs for the Cubs during the 2010s?

5. Whom did Joe Maddon succeed as manager of the Cubs?

6. Which team did the Cubs defeat in the 2015 National League Wild Card game?

7. Who won the World Series with the Royals in 2015 then again with the Cubs a year later?

8. Which team eliminated the Cubs after an epic, 13 inning 2018 Wild Card game?

9. Who was the only Cub to steal 30 or more bases in a single season during the 2010s?

10. The Cubs were involved in Major League Baseball's first tie in 11 years in a 2016 matchup against which team?

11. Which team did the Cubs defeat 3 games to 2 in the 2017 NLDS?

12. The 2017 Cubs lost the NLCS in five games to which club?

13. In 2015, who set the club record for the most RBIs by a Cubs rookie?

14. Which Cubs pitcher recorded the most saves during the 2010s?

15. Which pitcher recorded the most saves during the 2016 World Championship season?

16. Who was the only Cubs pitcher to record 20 wins in a season during the 2010s?

17. True of false – Attendances at Wrigley Field topped the 3 million mark every year during the 2010s?

18. Jake Arrieta joined the Cubs from which American League ballclub?

19. The longest game in franchise history took place on July 29, 2014. How long did it last? a) 4hr 27m b) 5hr 27m c) 6hr 27m

20. Who were the Cubs' opponent in that epic 2014 match-up? a) Colorado b) Milwaukee c) New York Mets

Quiz 17: Answers

1. Tampa Bay Rays 2. Kris Bryant 3. Ian Happ 4. Kerry Wood 5. David Bote 6. Kenny Lofton 7. Rick and Paul Reuschel 8. Arizona 9. Woodrow Wilson 10. True 11. Oakland 12. 1945 13. Detroit 14. Rod Beck 15. Sammy Sosa and Ryne Sandberg 16. Kris Bryant 17. #9 18. Claude Passeau 19. a) 101 games 20. b) 1948

Quiz 19: Pot Luck

1. Cubs fans used to throw 'Oh, Henry' chocolate bars onto the field when which player struck a home run?

2. In 2014, which Cub became the first player in 60 years to hit three home runs in his first three Major League appearances?

3. In May 1982, which Cubs pitcher became the seventh in Major League history to record 3,000 strikeouts?

4. Which National League club have the Cubs defeated the fewest times?

5. In May 2019, the Cubs enjoyed back-to-back walk off wins in successive games against which team?

6. Who was the team's general manager from July 2002 through to August 2011?

7. Do the Cubs have a winning or losing record in games played on Opening Day?

8. True or false – In 2010, the team published a book called 'Chicago Cubs Cookbook: All-Star Recipes from Your Favorite Players'?

9. Which relief pitcher tied a franchise record in a March 2003 game against the Mets after striking out six successive batters?

10. What did the Cubs do on May 10, 1997 that they haven't done since?

11. Who hit an extra innings, walk-off home run to give the Cubs a famous win over the Phillies on opening day of the 1969 season?

12. In 1975, who became the first, and so far, only, Cub to win the MVP Award at the All-Star Game?

13. The Cubs took part in the first MLB game outside of North America in March 2000. In which country did the historic game take place?

14. Who were the Cubs' opponent in this overseas series?

15. Sandy Koufax tossed a perfect game in a 1-0 win over the Cubs on September 9, 1965. Which Cubs pitcher gave the Dodgers just one hit in the same game?

16. Who hit a walk-off homer to give the Cubs a famous 4-3 win over the Nationals on Mother's Day 2016?

17. True or false – In a 1959 game against the Cards, the Cubs were involved in an incident that resulted in two balls being in play at the same time?

18. Sammy Sosa is one of two Cubs batters to hit more than 200 home runs on the road. Who is the other?

19. The Cubs led the National League in grand slams in 2019. How many did they hit? a) 10 b) 11 c) 12

20. On April 23, 2008, the Cubs recorded their 10,000th win in franchise history, defeating which team? a) Colorado b) Philadelphia c) San Diego

Quiz 18: Answers

1. Two 2. Aramis Ramirez 3. Starlin Castro 4. Anthony Rizzo 5. Rick Renteria 6. Pittsburgh 7. Ben Zobrist 8. Colorado 9. Tony Campana 10. Pittsburgh 11. Washington 12. L.A. Dodgers 13. Kris Bryant 14. Carlos Marmol 15. Hector Rondon 16. Jake Arrieta 17. False 18. Baltimore 19. c) 6hr 27m 20. a) Colorado

Quiz 20: Hall of Famers

1. Which Cub was the first player to win the NL MVP Award in back-to-back seasons?

2. Which Cubs Hall of Famer was named after a Yankees pitcher?

3. Which former Cubs pitcher was baseball's all-time leader in saves from 1993 through to 2006?

4. Which pitcher won 18 Gold Gloves in his stellar career which included two spells with the Cubs?

5. Which Hall of Famer drove in 937 runs during the 1960s, the most by any Cubs player?

6. Which former Cub was only the second player after Willie Mays to hit 400 home runs and steal 300 bases?

7. Which Hall of Famer hit four home runs for the Phillies in a game against the Cubs on April 17, 1976?

8. Which Cubs great was the first pitcher elected to the Hall of Fame who had never started a game?

9. Which Hall of Fame pitcher spent three seasons with the Cubs in the mid-80s, winning 27 games with an ERA of 3.63?

10. Which one-time Cub was the first Canadian player elected into the Baseball Hall of Fame?

11. Which fiery Hall of Fame pitcher, best known for his time with the Yankees, spent a single season with the Cubs in 1988?

12. 'My Sweet-Swinging Lifetime with the Cubs' was the title of which Hall of Famer's autobiography?

13. Which Hall of Fame-pitcher recorded his 300th career win while with the Mets in a game against the Cubs in 2007?

14. Which Hall of Fame-broadcaster spent the final 16 years of his career with the Cubs until his death in 1998?

15. Which legendary manager, who was elected into the Hall of Fame in 1994, was in the Cubs dugout between 1966 and 1972?

16. Which Cubs pitcher lost his index finger in a farming machine accident aged just five?

17. Which Hall of Famer spent three seasons with the Cubs before being traded to the Cardinals in a deal that brought Ernie Broglio to Chicago?

18. Which Hall of Fame manager appeared in a single game for the Cubs as a player, scoring the winning run as a pinch runner on opening day 1973?

19. By what name was pitcher Grover Cleveland Alexander better known? a) Old Pat b) Old Paul c) Old Pete

20. Up to 2020, how many Hall of Famers had the Cubs as their primary team? a) 14 b) 15 c) 16

Quiz 19: Answers

1. Henry Rodriguez 2. Javier Báez 3. Fergie Jenkins 4. Arizona 5. Miami 6. Jim Hendry 7. Winning 8. True 9. Juan Cruz 10. Turn a triple play 11. Willie Smith 12. Bill Madlock 13. Japan 14. New York Mets 15. Bob Hendley 16. Javier Báez 17. True 18. Ernie Banks 19. a) 10 grand slams 20. a) Colorado

Quiz 21: Pot Luck

1. Which Cubs catcher started for the National League in the 2008 All-Star Game?

2. Which three members of the Cubs' 2016 World Championship team had previously represented the USA in baseball at the 2008 Olympics?

3. Which infielder's streak of 141 errorless games in 2012 is the longest by a second baseman in club history?

4. In a May 1988 game against the Reds, who became the first Cubs pitcher in 79 years to throw a shutout on his Major League debut?

5. True or false – More than 2,000 different players have appeared for the Cubs throughout the history of the team?

6. Which first baseman went 150 games without committing an error across the 2017 and 2018 seasons?

7. Jason Hayward, Bill Buckner and Mark Prior all wore what number jersey?

8. Who hit a 10th inning walk-off homer to give the Cubs a 3-2 win over the Reds on August 24, 2018?

9. Which former Cub later went on to catch no-hitters from Dwight Gooden and David Cone while with the New York Yankees?

10. The Cubs claimed a dramatic 2-1 win in 15 innings over which division rival on May 11, 2019?

11. Which Cub hit the walk-off homer that secured that epic win?

12. In a 1971 game against the Cardinals, which pitcher became the first, and so far, only, Cubs draft pick to make his professional debut with the Major League team?

13. Which switch-hitter struck home runs from both sides of the plate in a May 7, 2018 game against the Marlins?

14. Fergie Jenkins was one of only two Cubs pitchers to enjoy a 20-win season during the 1970s. Who was the other?

15. Which Cubs catcher won a Silver Slugger award in 2005?

16. Who is said to have pointed to the Wrigley Field bleachers before hitting Charlie Root's next pitch for a home run in the 1932 World Series?

17. In 1951, which legendary golfer hit a golf ball from home plate that hit the famous Wrigley Field scoreboard?

18. Which future NFL quarterback did the Cubs select in the 43rd round of the 2009 MLB Draft?

19. The 2004 Cubs set a franchise record after hitting how many home runs? a) 233 b) 234 c) 235

20. What wording appears on the front of the Cubs road uniforms? a) Chicago b) Cubs c) None

Quiz 20: Answers

1. Ernie Banks 2. Ryne Sandberg 3. Lee Smith 4. Greg Maddux 5. Ron Santo 6. Andre Dawson 7. Mike Schmidt 8. Bruce Sutter 9. Dennis Eckersley 10. Fergie Jenkins 11. Goose Gossage 12. Billy Williams 13. Tom Glavine 14. Harry Caray 15. Leo Durocher 16. Mordecai Brown 17. Lou Brock 18. Tony La Russa 19. c) Old Pete 20. b) 15

Quiz 22: Nicknames

Match the nickname to the player.

1. Mad Dog   a) Fred McGriff

2. Mr Cub   b) Andre Dawson

3. El Mago (The Magician) c) Mark DeRosa

4. Wild Thing   d) Burt Hooton

5. The Pulse   e) Henry Blanco

6. The Crime Dog   f) Leo Durocher

7. Toothpick   g) Greg Maddux

8. Happy   h) David Ross

9. The Hawk   i) Ernie Banks

10. The Sweet Swinger   j) Rick Sutcliffe

11. The Professor   k) Dave Kingman

12. Grandpa Rossy   l) Leon Durham

13. Popeye   m) Sam Jones

14. The Sarge   n) Mitch Williams

15. Bull   o) Mordecai Brown

16. The Lip   p) Gary Matthews Sr

17. Kong   q) Billy Williams

18. Hank White   r) Javier Báez

19. Three Fingers   s) Don Zimmer

20. The Red Baron   t) Kyle Hendricks

Quiz 21: Answers

1. Geovany Soto 2. Dexter Fowler, Jake Arrieta and Trevor Cahill 3. Darwin Barney 4. Jeff Pico 5. True 6. Anthony Rizzo 7. #22 8. David Bote 9. Joe Girardi 10. Milwaukee 11. Willson Contreras 12. Burt Hooton 13. Ian Happ 14. Rick Reuschel 15. Michael Barrett 16. Babe Ruth 17. Sam Snead 18. Colin Kaepernick 19. c) 235 home runs 20. a) Chicago

Quiz 23: Pot Luck

1. The Cubs' #26 jersey number is retired in honor of which player?

2. Who are the two Cubs pitchers to have won Silver Slugger Awards?

3. At the close of the 2019 season, only one Major League franchise had more all-time regular season wins than the Cubs. Which one?

4. Which catcher was behind the plate for Kerry Wood's epic 20 strikeout game in 1998?

5. Sammy Sosa led the team in home runs on the 1998 playoff team. Who was second behind Sosa that year with 31 homers?

6. What country did Anthony Rizzo represent in the 2013 World Baseball Classic?

7. Which Cubs great played for the club between 1986 and 1992 then returned to Wrigley in 2004?

8. Who hit his first career walk-off homer on July 16, 2019 to give the Cubs a 4-3, 10th inning victory over the Reds?

9. What is the color of the Cubs' alternate jersey?

10. In 2004, four Cubs batters hit 30 or more home runs. Name the quartet.

11. Which pair of Cubs pitchers threw back-to-back one hitters in May 2001 games against Cincinnati and Milwaukee?

12. Which Cub set a Major League record in September 2007 after hitting seven leadoff home runs during the month?

13. Do the Cubs have a winning or losing record in games that have gone to extra innings?

14. 'One Dog' was the nickname of which former Cub who was with the club in the late 1990s?

15. Who holds the franchise record for the most saves in a single season by a right-handed pitcher?

16. Which Cubs pitcher famous brawled with Cincinnati's Paul Wilson in a game in June 2003?

17. Who are the fours Cubs bosses to have won the NL Manager of the Year Award?

18. Kris Bryant hit his first career Major League home run off which well-traveled Milwaukee pitcher?

19. Pitcher Larry Corcoran was the first Cubs player to do what? a) hit a grand slam b) pitch a shutout c) hit for the cycle

20. The 2018 Cubs set a team record after using how many different pitchers during the season? a) 31 b) 33 c) 35

Quiz 22: Answers

1. g) Greg Maddux 2. i) Ernie Banks 3. r) Javier Báez 4. n) Mitch Williams 5. c) Mark DeRosa 6. a) Fred McGriff 7. m) Sam Jones 8. d) Burt Hooton 9. b) Andre Dawson 10. q) Billy Williams 11. t) Kyle Hendricks 12. h) David Ross 13. s) Don Zimmer 14. p) Gary Matthews Sr 15. l) Leon Durham 16. f) Leo Durocher 17. k) Dave Kingman 18. e) Henry Blanco 19. o) Mordecai Brown 20. j) Rick Sutcliffe

Quiz 24: Anagrams

Rearrange the letters to make the name of a current or former Cub.

1. Briny Stark

2. I Rake Tea Jar

3. Mass Mayos

4. Energy Brands

5. Breaks Nine

6. A Zebra Jive

7. Max Grudged

8. Jaded Moon

9. Or Keyword

10. Join Rebel

11. Razor Mobs Canal

12. Noon Tsar

13. Redrew Felt Ox

14. Chalks Brewery

15. Landlord Issues

16. Jets Enrol

17. Dinky Hecklers

18. Crablike Grim

19. Wily Basil Mill

20. Hornet Condor

Quiz 23: Answers

1. Billy Williams 2. Carlos Zambrano and Jake Arrieta 3. The Giants 4. Sandy Martinez 5. Henry Rodriguez 6. Italy 7. Greg Maddux 8. Kyle Schwarber 9. Blue 10. Sammy Sosa, Derrek Lee, Aramis Ramirez, Moises Alou 11. Jon Lieber and Kerry Wood 12. Alfonso Soriano 13. Winning 14. Lance Johnson 15. Rod Beck 16. Kyle Farnsworth 17. Jim Frey, Don Zimmer, Lou Piniella and Joe Maddon 18. Kyle Lohse 19. a) Hit a grand slam 20. c) 35 pitchers

Quiz 25: Pot Luck

1. What color are the names and numbers on the back of the Cubs' home jersey?

2. In 2018, who became just the second Cubs second baseman to win a Silver Slugger Award?

3. Which former Chicago pitcher's career average of 10.32 strikeouts per nine innings is the second best in Major League history?

4. Whose 24 pinch hits during the 2018 season are the most in club history?

5. Which Cubs first baseman won Gold Glove honors in 1992, 1993, 1995 and 1996?

6. Which pitcher led the team with 19 wins during the 1998 playoff run?

7. Cubs superstar Anthony Rizzo was originally drafted by which organization?

8. Which Cubs pitcher hit a grand slam in a July 1998 game at the Braves?

9. Which outfielder, who previously won Rookie of the Year honors and who finished his pro career with the Cubs in 2005, has the longest surname in team history?

10. Which Cub was the first African-American pitcher to throw a no-hitter?

11. Which pinch-hitter smashed an 11th inning walk-off homer to give the Cubs a 1-0 win over the Royals on September 28, 2015?

12. In a pair of September 2006 matchups against the Reds, which Cubs rookie tossed consecutive complete games?

13. Derrek Lee and Luis Gonzalez both wore what number jersey?

14. True or false – The Cubs have had two different pitchers called Dutch Leonard, neither of whom was from the Netherlands?

15. Which rookie's prolific 2010 season ended prematurely after his chest was punctured by a broken bat?

16. Willson Contreras wears what number jersey?

17. Which Cub is on Twitter under the moniker @FaridYu?

18. Which Cubs catcher was ejected after punching Scott Podsednik during an infamous brawl with the White Sox in May 2006?

19. What is the fewest number of games the Cubs have won in a full season? a) 53 b) 55 c) 57

20. For a brief period in the early years of the franchise, the team was known as the Chicago...? a) Colts b) Magnums c) Revolvers

Quiz 24: Answers

1. Kris Bryant 2. Jake Arrieta 3. Sammy Sosa 4. Ryne Sandberg 5. Ernie Banks 6. Javier Báez 7. Greg Maddux 8. Joe Maddon 9. Kerry Wood 10. Jon Lieber 11. Carlos Zambrano 12. Ron Santo 13. Dexter Fowler 14. Kyle Schwarber 15. Addison Russell 16. Jon Lester 17. Kyle Hendricks 18. Craig Kimbrel 19. Billy Williams 20. Hector Rondon

Made in the USA
Monee, IL
06 December 2020